The cave home of Peking Man

D1178209

By Chia Lan-po

FOREIGN LANGUAGES PRESS
PEKING 1975

First edition   1975

Printed in the People's Republic of China

Site of Peking Man's cave home.

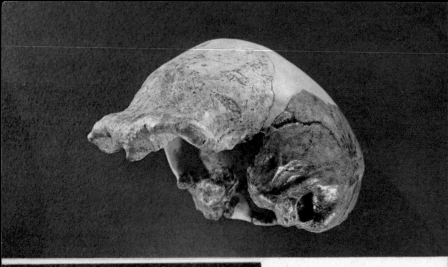

Peking Man skull-cap, excavated in 1966.

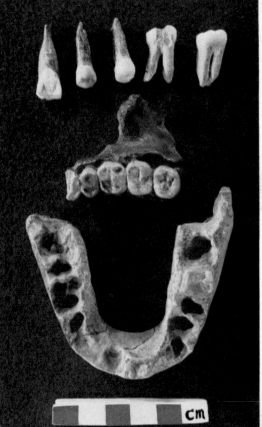

Peking Man: teeth (*above*), maxilla (*middle*) and mandible (*below*).

Points and scrapers fashioned and
used by Peking Man.

More points and scrapers.

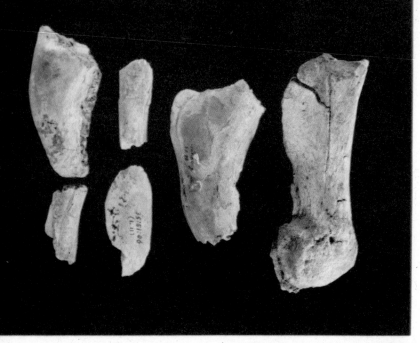

Charred bones unearthed from the cave deposit.

Scorched stones.

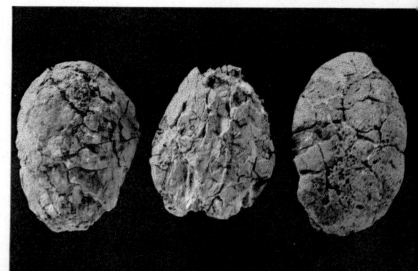

Contents

In lieu of a foreword

Dragon Bone Hill[1] near Choukoutien,[2] the cave home of Peking Man,[3] is famous all over the world. The site has yielded human fossils, artifacts made of bone or stone, and traces of the use of fire, that are roughly 500,000-200,000 years old. These have enriched the evidence for the study of the origin and evolution of the human species, attesting that it was man's ability to engage in labour that gave him birth.

In 1953, a small display centre for the finds was built here. In 1961, the State Council designated the area as one of China's major government-protected cultural sites. During the Great Proletarian Cultural Revolution, a new exhibition hall was erected in 1972.

Mountains tower above the cave site to the north and west. At their foot flows a stream, and below them to the south and southeast stretches a vast plain. The surroundings recall the precarious life of Peking Man who hunted in the primeval plains and forests, picked up and made tools and through his work, began a stubborn struggle

1

with nature. It was from a cave here on December 2, 1929 that Chinese workers and scientists dug up the first complete skull-cap of Peking Man.

Fossil remains of the Upper Cave Man,[4] dating back more than 15,000 years, were found in a cave further up the mountain above the cave of Peking Man. (The "absolute age" of the fossils recovered from the lower part of the deposits in this cave is about 18,340 B.P. according to a recent radiocarbon dating.) To date, the remains of eight persons of different ages have been found in this cave. They include three complete skulls and fragments of skeletons from a grave. Unearthed with them were mammalian fossils, bone and stone implements and ornaments such as perforated animal teeth, bivalve shells, stone beads, pebbles and fish bones, and grooved hollow bones.

A little to the west of the cave home of Peking Man stands the new exhibition hall, in which the Peking Man and Upper Cave Man finds are displayed. The exhibits begin with the origin of life, and man in his embryonic stage, showing that prior to the coming of human beings, there had been life on earth for more than three billion years, and that the evolutionary process was from the inorganic to the organic, from the simple to the complex, from the invertebrate to the vertebrate, from the aquatic to the terrestrial and from the oviparous to the viviparous. By means of specimens, pictures and narrative, the exhibition sets out the weighty evidence which proves that man evolved from certain vertebrates, themselves the descendants of invertebrates, and that the human species is the result of evolution.

Further on, the exhibition highlights the theme that man was created by his own labour. This section reveals the history of the earliest man and his evolution: how he developed from the southern ape (*Australopithecus*) to Java Man, Peking Man (*Homo erectus*), etc. and finally to modern man (*Homo sapiens*). Introduced in detail here is the life of Peking Man, his tool-making, use of fire, etc., which attest that the evolution of apes into men was brought about by social-productive labour, and that man's conscious initiative was continuously developed and elevated through practice.

The last section of the exhibition focuses on the progress and achievements made in paleoanthropology and vertebrate palaeontology in China after liberation. Many exhibits are new finds which provide very important evidence for anthropological and palaeontological studies.

---

[1]龙骨山. [2]周口店. [3]"北京人". [4]"山顶洞人".

The "home" of Peking Man

In the Peking area 50 kilometres southwest of the city proper, there is a small town called Choukoutien. It lies at the southeastern foot of the Western Hills, with mountains to its north and west, and rolling hills on its northeastern fringe. To the south and southeast the view opens onto the great North China Plain, which slopes gently away to the southeast. The Paerh River, actually a stream, emerges out of a narrow gorge not far north of Choukoutien to flow along the west side of the town. It then meanders southwards to meet the Liuli River about ten kilometres away and on to empty into the sea near Tientsin.

Opposite Choukoutien on the west bank of the Paerh River are two round-topped limestone hills which stand in an east-to-west line. The one to the east, known as Lungkushan or Dragon Bone Hill, has a cave on its northern slope, in which the fossil remains of Peking Man, artifacts, traces of the use of fire and a variety of animal bones were found. These finds show us how Peking Man, intelligent and hardworking, struggled indefatigably against nature to create a primeval culture in China.

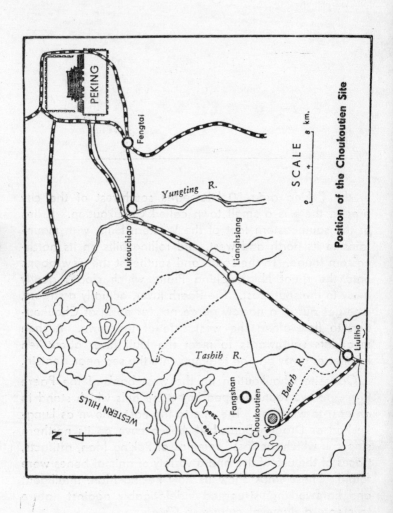

Position of the Choukoutien Site

SCALE

0   4   8 km.

PEKING

Fengtai

Yungting R.

Lukouchiao

Lianghsiang

Tashih R.

Baerh R.

Liuliho

Fangshan

Choukoutien

WESTERN HILLS

200

400

N

Reconstruction of Peking Man.

Cave home of Peking Man. ▲   Part of the cave. ▶

A corner of the exhibition hall at Choukoutien.

In the more remote past, 450 million years ago, the Choukoutien area was part of a sea as the presence there of Ordovician limestone proves. In this period marine invertebrates flourished and the earliest types of fish had also emerged. These fish were so primitive that they had no mandible, or lower jaw. As a result of crustal movement, the sea gave way to plain and mountain. Roughly 300 million years ago, the warm and humid climate in this region produced an abundance of vegetation. Vertebrates further developed; amphibians were gradually becoming more numerous and primitive reptiles whose habitat was terrestrial had appeared.

About eight million years ago in the early Pliocene, the topography of the Choukoutien area was still quite different from what it is today. One piece of evidence of this is that on a slope one and half kilometres south of the town, a large number of fossil fish have been found 70 metres above the present river bed. Clearly the slope was once the bank of an ancient river, whose bed sank as a result of the gradual elevation of the surrounding land. Formerly, the hill west of Dragon Bone Hill and the mountains further west were probably part of the same range. Later, however, they became independent formations as a result of prolonged weathering and erosion. The stream to the east of the Dragon Bone Hill was once much wider. There is evidence that even the town of Choukoutien was a part of the river bed. Gravel, pebbles and boulders left by the old river abound on the western slope of the Taiping Hill east of the town, and also along the southeastern foot of the Shengping Hill north of the Dragon Bone Hill.

Through crustal movement, the thick limestone rock formation was warped upward. Limestone is soluble, and where folding has occurred, is especially liable to erosion by groundwater; hence caves and fissures formed here.

Prior to excavation, the cave that Peking Man dwelt in was filled with layers of deposit. Its dimensions are now roughly estimated to have been 140 metres from east to west, and 40 metres from south to north at the eastern end which was the broadest part, while at the western end the width narrowed down to a mere 2.5 metres. The fossiliferous deposit is more than 40 metres deep. There was once a roof over a large part of the cave, but due to weathering and erosion, only traces of it were found in the eastern half of the cave.

The deposit is straticulated, with 13 layers each distinguished by certain characteristics. Thus the whole deposit reads like a history of Peking Man, the finds in each layer being an authentic record providing the basis for this booklet.

At the very bottom of the cave, beneath the fossiliferous deposit is a layer of gravel and reddish silt, generally referred to as the basal-gravel layer. This gravel consists mostly of rounded pebbles, but some of it still shows traces of glaciation and is considered glacier-formed. Sporopollen analyses have confirmed that this layer was deposited during an age of cold climate, evidence of a glacial period prior to the arrival of Peking Man.

Overlaying this basal-gravel layer is a stratum of reddish mud deposited when the water was less turbulent, and in it stone implements have been found, indicating that man had already come to the cave at that time. Since no human fossil has been found along with these artifacts, their owner cannot yet be identified. It is believed that they belong to Peking Man, as they indicate a level of skill similar to that which would be required to make tools proved to be his, although the mammalian fossil remains found in this layer belong to an earlier period than the deposit which yielded the Peking Man fossils. The first inhabitants of this cave do not seem to have stayed long, for no artifacts other than the few stone implements have been found.

On top of the reddish mud deposit is a layer of coarse sand, evidence of a big flood in the area. When the flood receded, cave-dwelling Chinese hyenas, an extinct species, were the first visitors. This sandy layer has yielded a large number of hyena skeletons and a layer of coprolites, or fossilized dung. These hyenas had the distinctive habit of excreting at a fixed spot and their diet consisted mainly of carrion. With their powerful jaws and teeth they could crack and chew even the hardest animal bones. This meant that their excretum was rich in bone, and thus well suited to fossilization.

Peking Man took over the cave not long after these hyenas. His bones and those of other animals, as well as his tools of bone and stone and traces of his use of fire are to be found in this layer.

In the middle section of the 40-metre-deep deposit, large quantities of hyena bone and coprolite again appear, indicating that the cave was occupied by this animal more than once. The presence of fine sand in several layers of this section proves that the area had been repeatedly flooded. In these layers, which contain an abundance of hyena-coprolite and sand, no skeletal remains of Peking Man have been found and artifacts are scarce. The assumption is that Peking Man occupied the cave only periodically, and that his occupation of it was interrupted at least four times.

The precise duration of his stay, from when he first inhabited the cave to his final departure is not known, but comparative studies of other reliably-dated sites roughly contemporary to the Choukoutien cave point to a period lasting about 300,000 years (500,000-200,000 B.P.). It is unlikely that Peking Man inhabited the cave generation after generation over such a long period. In all probability some of this type of men lived in the cave for a time and were then forced to move on to seek greener pasture as a result of changes in the climate, or for other reasons. Many years probably elapsed before another group came in.

Discovery and excavation

The first discoverers of this site of fossils were local lime-kiln workers. The place had long been quarried for lime-stone and the workers frequently came across fossils at their work sites. They called these objects "dragon bones," and hence the name Dragon Bone Hill. First, in 1918, fossils of birds and small mammals were found at a place not far southwest of the town of Choukoutien. Local people named the place Chicken Bone Hill.

A bigger and more abundant site, now known as the home of Peking Man, came to light in 1921, and for a short time excavations were made. In 1923, two human teeth, one a worn and fossilized human upper molar, and the other an unerupted lower permanent premolar were recovered. Later on, in 1927, a left permanent molar was found. Anthropologists concluded chiefly on the basis of this evidence that it belonged to a human genus not yet identified. The new genus was given the name *Sinanthropus*. Later on, as more evidence was collected, they coined a name for the species, *pekinenesis*. Thus the complete scientific term became *Sinanthropus pekinenesis*, and the expression Peking Man used in this book is simply the popular name for this species of man.

Discovery of the three teeth at Choukoutien attracted wide attention from academic circles everywhere, and spurred on the extensive excavations that followed.

Excavation before liberation

The systematic excavation of the Choukoutien treasure trove began in 1927. That year saw the discovery of the well-preserved left lower molar mentioned above. In 1928, several more human teeth, the greater part of a juvenile mandible and an adult mandible fragment bearing three teeth were unearthed. But the evidence so far was still deemed insufficient to establish Peking Man on a solid scientific basis. On December 2, 1929, this was finally achieved when the first well-preserved skull-cap of Peking Man was discovered by Chinese workers and scientists. News of this aroused great interest among scholars throughout the world.

A veteran worker who participated in the excavation gave this account of it:

"It all took place after 4 o'clock in the afternoon. We had got down about 30 metres deep and only three men could stand at the bottom of the hole. It was there the skull-cap was sighted, half of it embedded in loose earth, the other half in hard clay. The sun had almost set and the light was getting poorer. The team debated whether to take it out right away or to wait until the next day when they could see better. The agonizing suspense of a whole night was felt to be too much to bear, so they decided to go on. It was well done. A small piece of the bone cracked in the course of the digging, but no serious damage was done, and the restoration was easy. The whole piece had to be dried to make it firm enough to take to the research unit in Peking. The best method then available was drying out over a charcoal fire, and that was how it was done. This process took a day and two whole nights."

The importance of a skull-cap lies in the fact that it possesses the salient characteristics from which scientists may discern the relationship of its owner to other known human fossils and establish his lineage. That was why the new find was considered so momentous.

From then until 1937, a large number of fossil remains of Peking Man, his stone implements and evidence of his use of fire were found at the site. In a nearby cave, fossil remains of the Upper Cave Man and many traces of his culture were unearthed.

It should be pointed out that although all these finds were made at sites around Peking, since China was then ruled by a reactionary government, Chinese personnel were excluded from research work on human fossils. More regrettable still, the human fossils recovered prior to the War of Resistance Against Japan (1937-1945), including those of the Peking Man, the Upper Cave Man and some of the highly valuable primate remains, have disappeared in the hands of certain Americans.

Excavation after liberation

Soon after the liberation of Peking in 1949, the excavation at Choukoutien was resumed after a 12-year interruption, as the Chinese Communist Party and the People's Government attached great importance to the work. The first few digs yielded large numbers of artifacts and animal bones along with five more teeth of Peking Man, a humerus, or upper arm bone, and tibia, or shin-bone. This was the first time a tibia of Peking Man had been found.

Although excavation itself was suspended at Choukoutien between 1952 and 1955 because so many other archaeological sites throughout China awaited exploration, activity continued around the home of Peking Man. A reafforestation programme was carried out on the bare hillsides, and a small display centre was erected. In 1955, a new paved road which leads right up to the foot of Dragon Bone Hill connecting the city proper with Choukoutien was constructed. And in 1972, the display centre was expanded into an exhibition hall to assist the broad masses in their study of dialectical and historical materialism. Now Choukoutien is a well-known place drawing many Chinese and foreign visitors every year.

In 1956-57, under the auspices of the Institute of Vertebrate Paleontology and Paleoanthropology[1] of the Chinese Academy of Sciences, two seminar courses were held at Choukoutien on the excavation and restoration of vertebrate fossils. The purpose was to improve and promote the excavation and protection of human and mammalian fossils in China. The participants were young museum and government workers concerned with such tasks. They came from many provinces and municipalities, and are now applying the knowledge they acquired in their jobs.

In the course of their training, they did some practice excavation at two sites in Choukoutien, Locality 15 and Locality 13, which had both been excavated before.

Locality 15 is situated on the southeastern slope of Dragon Bone Hill, 70 metres from the Peking Man cave. Though this was not a new excavation, it still yielded quite a lot. Like the home of Peking Man, this is a cave too, but the roof collapsed when the deposit was accumulating, and is no longer extant. The deposit is uniformly composed of breccia, in which fossil vertebrates, stone implements and traces of the use of fire such as ashes and charred bones were all found, but not human fossils. As these finds compare closely with those in the upper layers of the Peking Man cave, it is evident that in the later period of his occupation of Choukoutien, Peking Man lived in this cave as well.

Locality 13 is situated on a low limestone slope 50 metres above the river bed and one kilometre from the cave of Peking Man. Excavation began here before liberation. But this investigation still produced a large number of objects from a fissure extending eastward. Among these were complete fossils of Merck's rhinoceros, the woolly rhinoceros and giant deer with palm-like antlers. Other important finds were: a small chopper of chert pebble with a fluted edge, several artificially-shaped quartz flakes and traces of the use of fire. Judging by the characteristics of the fossil vertebrates found here, these animals are roughly contemporary to the mud layer which overlays the gravel bottom of the cave of Peking Man and therefore predate the layers of deposit which yielded the Peking Man fossil remains. No human fossil was found, but it may be inferred that Peking Man lived here before he settled down in his cave home.

In 1958, during China's Big Leap Forward, Peking Man's cave home again became a major excavation site. A more refined interpretation of the entire mass of deposits resulted. Particularly noteworthy is the discovery of a triangular stone flake in the mud layer overlaying the gravel bottom of the cave. The flake, chipped at the edge into a chopper, was taken from a huge chert core. Like the chert chopper found at Locality 13, this is also a specimen of the earliest stone implement so far unearthed in the Choukoutien area.

As the excavation continued, another valuable discovery was made in 1959. It was a well-preserved mandible of Peking Man embedded in a hard-earth layer 27 metres deep at the northeastern part of the cave. The teeth were gone except for a fragment of a molar still attached at the left side. But it was the first complete mandible of Peking Man unearthed, and as such, it provided important evidence for the reconstruction of his jawbone.

In 1966 during the Great Proletarian Cultural Revolution, excavation shifted to the top layer in the eastern section lying below the mouth of the Upper Cave. This locality had, in 1934, yielded a left temporal bone and parts of the occipital and parietal bones that were attached. In 1966, on two successive days — May 4 and 5 — more fragments of occipital and frontal bones were found, and they fitted very well into the model based on the head bones previously unearthed, thus producing a fairly complete skull-cap. When this restored skull-cap was compared with the ones which were found in the lower levels, certain differences could be seen. Contrary to what was once believed, therefore, paleoanthropologists now think that there do exist signs of evolution between early and late Peking Man.

Peking Man skull-cap, excavated in 1929, the first time a Peking Man skull-cap had been discovered.

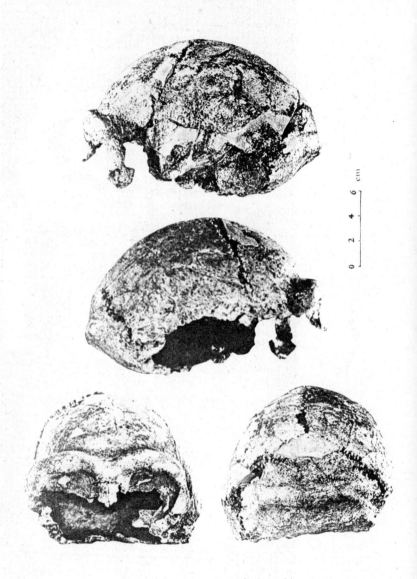

Skull-cap found in 1936.

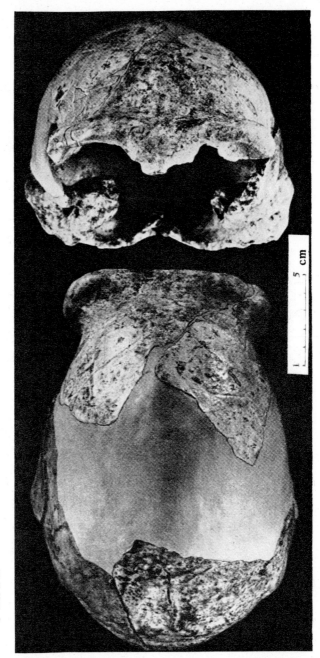

Skull-cap found in 1966. *Top*: a frontal view; *bottom*: viewed from above.

5 cm

Site of the 1966
skull-cap find.

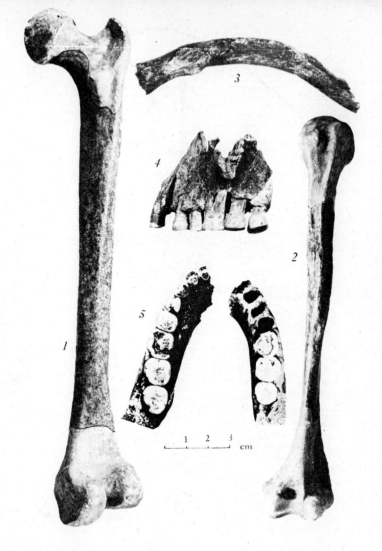

Bones of Peking Man: (1) Right femur (thighbone) of an adult male, total length: 407 mm. The lighter colour indicates reconstructed parts. (2) Frontal view of a left humerus (upper arm bone) of an adult male, total length: 324 mm. The lighter colour indicates reconstructed parts. (3) Frontal view of a clavicle (collar bone), unreconstructed. The length would be 145 mm. after reconstruction. (4) Maxilla (upper jawbone). (5) Right and left parts of mandible.

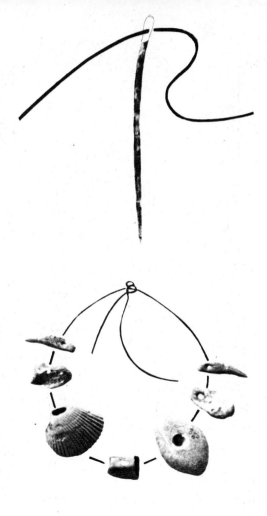

Bone needle and some ornaments used by the Upper Cave Man.

Reconstruction of the Upper Cave Man.

The years of extensive excavation at Peking Man's cave home have involved the removal of some 240,000 cubic metres of deposit, yet this is only 40 per cent of the estimated total. The site has yielded a great number of human fossils and artifacts as well as mammalian fossil remains. Studies made on all these objects have contributed to a better understanding of the physical characteristics of Peking Man, his culture and social life, and the environs of Choukoutien in his time.

---

¹古脊椎动物与古人类研究所。

The position of Peking Man in human evolution

How did man originate

The discovery of Peking Man at Choukoutien attracted world-wide attention as it supplies important clues for tracing the origin of the human species. On this question, there has always been sharp controversy between the materialist and idealist schools.

In primitive society, due to the very low level of economic productivity, man could understand neither the complicated natural phenomena he encountered nor his own origin, and that gave rise to all kinds of myths. Ancient Chinese books have recorded the legend of a goddess Nuwa[1] who created man by shaping clay. The Christian Bible also has it that "God created man." The exploiting classes have used these legends to dupe and fetter the working people.

As society has developed, humankind has, through practice, accumulated scientific knowledge. About the middle of the 19th century, Charles Robert Darwin (1809-1882), an English naturalist, confirmed the theory that man had evolved from apes in the remote past, and that both man and ape derive from a common ancestor. This dealt a fatal blow to the fallacies that "God created man" and that species are immutable. However, limited by their historical conditions, Darwin and his followers did not recognize the decisive role played by labour in the origin of man. They did not understand that man differs in essence from other animals as they regarded man simply as one of the members of the biological world.

Soon after Darwin had advanced his theory, Frederick Engels (1820-1895), revolutionary teacher of the proletariat, acknowledged the great achievement of the naturalist in his work on the evolution of species and the origin of man, while pointing out the inadequacies of Darwin's theory. Basing his view on dialectical and historical materialism and on abundant evidence, Engels established the proposition that **"labour created man himself."*** This great thesis correctly explained the origin of man. The story of Peking Man which we tell in this booklet provides sound evidence for the thesis.

It is correct to say that modern man and the ape are both derived from a common ancestor, as is amply testified by anatomy, physiology and embryology. Who then was this common ancestor? This is a question of tremendous general interest still being explored by scientists. One thesis held that he might have been *Propliopithecus*, an ancestor of both ape and man, who lived 30,000,000 years ago. Another suggested the Egyptian ape, *Aegypto-pithecus*, of the same antiquity. This genus is believed to

---

* *Dialectics of Nature*, Eng. ed., Foreign Languages Publishing House, Moscow, 1966, p. 170.

have pursued two separate courses of evolution, of which one led to the great ape, *Dryopithecus*, from whom modern chimpanzee, the gorrilla and perhaps the orangutan developed. The other led to modern man through the stages of *Ramapithecus* (a kind of fossil-ape), *Australopithecus* (the most primitive of the known hominids), *Homo erectus* (including the sub-species, Peking Man) and the early *Homo sapiens*.

The difference between man and ape lies in the ability to make tools. As Engels said, **"No simian hand has ever fashioned even the crudest stone knife."*** From the known evidence, it was the genus of *Australopithecus* which began making tools. Thus the evolution of man may be roughly divided into three major stages, *Australopithecus*, *Homo erectus* and *Homo sapiens*, which last includes the modern man.

Fossils of *Australopithecus* were first reported in 1924 from South Africa, hence the name, which means southern ape. They lived mainly in the early Pleistocene, three to one million years ago. Fossils of this primate, belonging to no less than 90 individuals, have been found in South and East Africa. Stone implements from the early Pleistocene, the age in which the man-ape of South Africa (*Australopithecus africanus*) lived, have been found in Africa as well as at sites in Menton in France, in Bugiulesti in Romania and in China in Nihowan,[2] Yangyuan County,[3] Hopei Province, and in Hsihoutu Village,[4] Juicheng County,[5] Shansi Province. This indicates that ancestral men spread widely over the continents of Africa, Europe and Asia.

---

* Ibid., p. 171.

The hominids reached the stage of *Homo erectus*, a sub-species to which Peking Man belonged, in the Middle Pleistocene roughly 1,000,000 to 100,000 years ago. They are closer to the modern man than *Australopithecus*. Their fossil remains have been discovered at sites in Tanzania, Algeria, Morocco, Germany, the Indonesian island of Java and other places as well as in China at Choukoutien and Lantien.

In the past, anthropologists were often quick to name not only new species, but even new genera to accommodate their new-found fossil men, as for example with the fossils of the australopithecines. Thus, the name *"Pithecanthropus erectus"* was coined for Java Man; *"Sinanthropus pekinensis"* for Peking Man; and *"Atlanthropus mauritanicus"* for the fossil men discovered in Algeria.

Since the 1940s, all human fossils have been grouped under one generic name, *Homo*, as one species, while the differences between them are identified by sub-specific names. Thus the scientific term for the Java Man is now *Homo erectus erectus*, and Peking Man, *Homo erectus pekinensis*. These new names which clearly indicate the close relationship between them are internationally accepted.

Homo erectus, to which Peking Man belongs, was the link between *Australopithecus* and *Homo sapiens* in the course of evolution from ape to modern man.

Homo sapiens, a new man, emerged about 100,000 years ago. The title covers two sub-species. Following the time sequence of their appearance, one is given the name *Homo sapiens neanderthalensis* (the Neanderthal man) and the other *Homo sapiens sapiens* (the modern man).

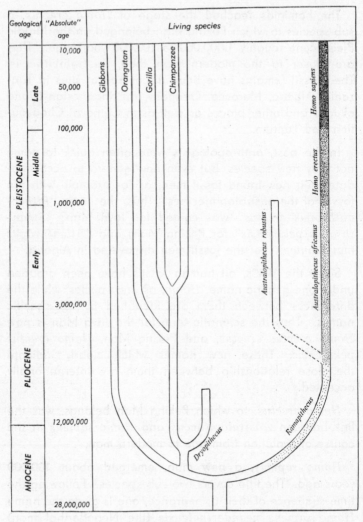

Geological age	"Absolute" age
	10,000
Late	50,000
	100,000
Middle	1,000,000
Early	
	3,000,000
PLIOCENE	12,000,000
MIOCENE	28,000,000

PLEISTOCENE

Living species

Gibbons
Orangutan
Gorilla
Chimpanzee

Homo sapiens
Homo erectus
Australopithecus robustus
Australopithecus africanus
Ramapithecus
Dryopithecus

Time-Chart of Man's Evolution

Neanderthal man lived 100,000 to 40,000 years ago. His remains have been found at sites widely scattered over Africa, Europe and Asia, though not yet in the other continents. In China, human fossils of the same period have come to light at Tingtsun Village,[6] Hsiangfen County,[7] Shansi Province; Hsiachungchiawan Village,[8] Changyang County,[9] Hupeh Province; and Mapa,[10] Shaokuan City,[11] Kwangtung Province.

About 40,000 years ago, man had acquired the characteristics he possesses today, and entered the stage of *Homo sapiens sapiens*, which includes the Upper Cave Man and all modern men. By then, he could already make fire and sew pelt garments, which aided his dispersion over the world. Fossils and artifacts of this species have been found on some islands and in all the continents except the Antarctica. As early as 10,000 years ago, man had reached the fringes of the Arctic Circle, and was using bows and arrows, snares and spears for hunting, and horn harpoons for fishing. At this time, there existed not only a variety of ornaments, but also carvings, paintings, clay figures and man-made dwellings.

From *Australopithecus* to *Homo erectus* and *Homo sapiens* of our day, the course of human evolution has taken about three million years, and Peking Man was but an episode in the long history of the development of man.

The characteristics of Peking Man

The total fossil remains of Peking Man unearthed at the Choukoutien cave amount to 6 complete skull-caps, 9 skull fragments, 6 pieces of facial bone, 15 mandibles, 152 teeth, 7 fragmented limb bones (humerus, clavicle, lunatum, femur, tibia, etc.) belonging to upwards of 40 persons.

These figures may make the material seem insufficient, or even fragmentary, yet as a whole, it is remarkable both in quantity and variety compared with the remains of Peking Man's contemporaries found elsewhere in the world. The fossils of *Homo erectus* found in Java, considered by anthropologists to be more primitive than Peking Man, were the remains of about 10 people, and this site has not yet yielded any stone implements associated with human fossils. Other remains roughly corresponding in age with those of Peking Man which have been found in Tanzania, Morocco, Algeria and Germany are even more scanty.

The Choukoutien materials have provided reliable information for the study of the physical characteristics of Peking Man. He had a low, flat, receding forehead. His skull was at its widest a little above the line of the auditory meatus (ear openings), lower than is the case with modern man. The skull was low-vaulted, about twice as thick as that of the modern man, and had a large occipital protuberance. His brow jutted out over his eye sockets like eaves over a house. His cranial capacity was on average 1,075 c.c., 73 per cent of that of the modern man, but bigger than that of the australopithecinae whose cranial capacity at most was only 56 per cent that of Peking Man. Peking Man had high, flat cheekbones and broad nasal bones, indicating that his nose must have been wide, and his face flat.

The mandibles varied in dimension, those of males were larger than those of females. The jaw is protruding and chinless in conspicuous contrast to modern man, who has a receding jaw and prominent chin. The lower dental arch of the apes is U-shaped formed by parallel rows of teeth, whereas in modern man the rows get gradually wider apart towards the back of the mouth. In Peking Man, who lies between these two in evolution, the ends of the dental arch are less widely separated than is the case with modern man, but less close to each other than in the ape.

The teeth of the Peking Man, both crowns and roots, are larger than those of modern man. The crown of the molar of Peking Man is very short in proportion to its width and length. Its grinding surface is more complicated with more cusps than that of the modern man. In the course of evolution, man's teeth became smaller and simpler in structure.

Not many of Peking Man's limb bones have been found, and of those which have been, most are fragments, fewer and less complete than the skull bones we have. Nevertheless, it is possible to determine the general characteristics of Peking Man's limbs by studying these fragments. Taking his fossil remains as a whole, his limb bones seem to have been more advanced than his skull.

His leg bones — the femur (thighbone) and the tibia (shinbone) — are in the main similar to those of modern man in size, form, muscular attachment and the proportion of the parts to each other. However they still have some primitive features such as a small medullary (marrow) cavity and thick wall. The medullary cavity of the femur is one-third the minimum diameter of the bone's shaft, whereas in modern man, it is one half. The fore-and-aft diameter of the middle section of the femur is smaller than its transverse diameter, whereas in modern man, the reverse is the case. Peking Man's tibia has a much smaller medullary cavity than that of modern man, and the shaft is far more rounded at the front. On the whole, Peking Man was a little bowlegged, but there is no doubt that he walked upright.

The arm bones including the humerus (upper arm bone), clavicle (collarbone) and lunatum (a wristbone), unlike the bones of the lower limbs, closely resemble those of modern man, except in the primitive features they still retain: a narrow medullary cavity and a thicker wall. This similarity shows that through labour, Peking Man had come to use his hands and arms almost as aptly as modern man.

The physical features of Peking Man may seem incongruous, since his limbs were more developed than his head. Two explanations of this have been advanced. One postulates that two kinds of "man" lived in the Choukoutien area, one of whom was the genuine human who made the tools and used fire. This kind is supposed to have preyed on the more backward Peking Man who lived in the same area, as it did on other animals, dragging them into his cave to eat and leaving the bones. This postulation is hardly worth discussing. Half a million years ago, no such "genuine human" had appeared. Years of excavation at Choukoutien have yielded nothing, not even a tooth to imply that two such different kinds existed. Chinese paleoanthropologists offer another explanation. It was because Peking Man laboured with his hands that his upper and lower limbs developed unevenly, with his upper limbs in the lead, nearer to those of modern man. The brain and the cranium, which developed gradually following on the evolution of the limbs, naturally retained more primitive features.

Could Peking Man speak? We think so. The convolutions of his brain as revealed by the model moulded with his skull indicate that he could. Besides, language would have been indispensable to Peking Man as a social animal engaged in systematic labour. In fact, language did not originate with Peking Man, it had appeared much earlier. As Engels said, **"Comparison with animals proves that this explanation of the origin of language from and in the process of labour is the only correct one."*** On the one hand man's ability to engage in labour enabled him to begin to transform nature, and on the other, labour demanded that members of a society work together and co-operate; thus language developed along with tool-making. Without such a means of communication, the first techniques of tool-making could not have been handed down to posterity, let alone improved upon.

Peking Man's language was probably still in an embryonic stage and undoubtedly had to be supplemented with many gestures. But it must have evolved well beyond the stage of the first few syllables, because he was already far in advance of his remote ancestor who had made the first tools, and had truly become a human being in behaviour. He is commonly called an ape-man only because of the simian aspects of his outward appearance.

---

* Ibid., p. 173.

[1]女娲. [2]泥河湾. [3]阳原县. [4]西侯度村. [5]芮城县. [6]丁村. [7]襄汾县. [8]下钟家湾. [9]长阳县. [10]马坝. [11]韶关市.

The artifacts of Peking Man

Stone implements

Many thousands of stone implements were found with the fossils of Peking Man and various vertebrates. At first glance they appear to be ordinary stones but close examination reveals signs left by human effort, unlike any that could have been caused naturally. These artifacts are evidence of Peking Man's ability to make quite a range of tools, using a variety of methods and materials. Engels said, **"Labour begins with the making of tools."*** Peking Man's ability to make tools shows that he could not only adapt himself to his environment and make use of nature, but had also begun consciously to transform it.

The raw materials used by Peking Man for making tools were hard minerals and rocks from outside his cave. They included rock crystal, vein quartz, flint, opal, sandstone and quartzite. Rock crystal was obtained from granite hills

* Ibid., p. 176.

Peking Man's tools: sandstone choppers.

Chert chopper excavated from the 13th layer, towards the bottom of the cave deposit, one of the earliest stone tools discovered here to date.

(1) Disc-scraper in chert. (2 & 3) Big scrapers with concave edges in quartzite and green sandstone. (4) Multi-edged chert scraper. (5) Point in vein quartz.

(1 & 2) Quartzite points.   (3) Double-shouldered point in flint.
(4) Double-edged scraper in green sandstone.   (5 & 6) Flint
disc-scrapers.   (7) Small flint chopper.

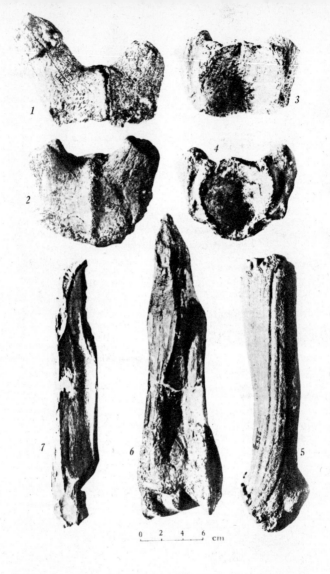

(1-4) Two sika deer skulls from which the antlers, facial bones and cranial base have been hacked to form "drinking bowls." (1) & (2) show the skulls from above, while (3) & (4) show their interiors. (5) Hammer made from the antler of a thick-jaw deer. (6) Point made from the lateral bone of the lower part of a deer's forelimb. (7) Knife-shaped bone implement.

more than two kilometres from the cave, and the rest from a nearby river bed.

We know from the stone implements found in the cave that Peking Man often selected oval-shaped pebbles to make single-or double-edged axes. These, known as choppers or chopping tools by archaeologists, were used for cutting firewood or shaping hunting clubs. They have been found in almost all the layers of the cave deposit. Most of these chopping tools are made of sandstone, and they vary in shape, from round discs to irregular triangles and long slabs.

Scientists have tried these tools out, and have found that using a chopper with roughly a 40°-angle edge it is possible to cut a piece of wood as thick as a human arm in half in about five minutes. They are easily blunted because of the material they are made of and then they have to be sharpened. This is why they look as if they have been chipped many times over, like a knife which has been honed too often. Many of the choppers which were found in the cave are blunt though they bear the signs of having been repeatedly sharpened. These seem to have been thrown away as worn-out stubs.

Chopping tools were not the only kind of tools used by Peking Man, scrapers were just as common. Mostly made of vein quartz flakes, these scrapers vary in size and shape. Their edges may be straight, convex, concave, or disc-like. Some are multi-edged. Big scrapers with concave edges could be used for shaping hunting clubs and the small ones with similar edges were probably household utensils. One common feature of the scrapers is that with a very few exceptions only one side of the flake was chipped.

Small scrapers were found in all layers of the deposit, but there were more of them in the upper layers. On the whole, Peking Man's stone implements tended to become smaller but more numerous as time went on. The most finely-made were the pointed stone tools. Only about a hundred of these have been found so far, of which 73 per cent are made of vein quartz. These tools show that Peking Man could chip and fashion stone fairly well. To make a point he had to split off a flake from a larger stone, then trim it all the way round until a slender point was achieved. This was the standard method regardless of the size and thickness of the point.

What purpose did these points serve? Scientists have not reached agreement on this. Some believe they were used for skinning animals, some think that they were used to dig worms out from under the bark of trees or to get the meat and marrow from animal bones. Anyway though one of these may have been the major function, these finer tools were probably used for many purposes.

Among the finds were also stone hammers and anvils. There were two kinds of hammer. One, oval in shape, was used to chip flakes off the edge of larger chunks, hence one end appears nicked through knocking. The incidence of scars on the axe head shows that Peking Man already had a preference for working with his right hand. The other kind of axe, generally made of fat, rounded stones, was used to strike upon quartz which had been placed on an anvil. Both these hammers and the anvils appear pitted.

In brief, the variety of Peking Man's stone implements, especially his points, and the level of skill he had achieved, are probably unmatched among comparable finds from that period.

Bone implements

Very few of the animal bones retrieved from the cave were in one piece. This may be attributed to a variety of causes, but one that nobody doubts is that a large number of these fragments are tools which Peking Man fashioned.

Fragments of antlers which were found in the cave had clearly been hacked up into short pieces. Antler roots are large and tough enough to serve as hammers; while the tines, being sharp, could be used for digging. The deep criss-crossed scratches on the tines show that they were in fact so used. Antlers are made of a very hard substance, which is not easy to cut. If a weak spot is first developed by scorching, and then hacked at with tools, the job is less difficult. It seems that Peking Man already knew this, for many of the pieces of antler in the cave appear to have been scorched at the ends. Also among the finds are the skulls of sika and thick-jaw deer, but very few of these are complete. Many of the skulls consist now only of brain-cases, the facial bones, antlers and cranium bases having been hacked off as the scars on these bones clearly reveal. Some of the skulls show that they had undergone repeated whittling. As well over a hundred specimens have been discovered, all similarly shaped, it is reasonable to infer that they served as "drinking bowls." Even the complete brain-cases of Peking Man himself so far recovered retain similar characteristics and probably served the same purpose.

Spikes and tools in knife-form made of the limb bones of deer and buffalo were probably used for grubbing up tubers or other edibles. The "knives" were made by first splitting a long bone, then fashioning it into the desired form. They seem to have been hammered into shape.

The implements of Peking Man, whether in stone or in bone, are far more advanced than those of his precursors, e.g., the *Australopithecus*. The types of tool are more clearly differentiated, better finished and are greater in variety. To our eyes of course, they are primitive and crude, yet with these tools, Peking Man waged an arduous struggle against nature. Each of these tools is symbolic of the difference between human society and a community of gregarious apes — the presence of labour. The Marxist dictum that **"labour created man himself"*** is indeed an irrefutable truth.

---

* Ibid., p. 170.

The use of fire — a milestone in human history

The use of fire was a milestone in human history. Some people have argued that man began making fire by boring wood. The legend in the ancient books of China about a man named Sui Jen Shih who invented this method belongs to this tradition. The discovery of charred substances in the cave of Peking Man pushed back the recorded history of man's use of fire many hundreds of thousands of years.

There can be no doubt about the Peking Man's use of fire; the evidence is all there. There are four thick layers of ash in the cave deposit. The uppermost of these overlays a huge limestone rock 5 metres thick, and 12 metres wide from east to west, which covers the cave floor completely from north to south. Evidently this rock is a part of the collapsed cave roof, and the deposit accumulated on it only after it fell in, leaving the cave open to the sky. Peking Man then made both his home and his hearth here on this stone slab. The fact that the ash was not spread over the whole of the slab's surface, but was found in two piles shows that Peking Man not only used fire, but could also control it, confining it to a specific place.

The thickest layer of ash, in the upper-middle part of the cave deposit, is up to six metres deep. Stone tools and fossilised small vertebrates — rats and bats — were numerous in this layer, sometimes indeed forming their own layers. The ash deposit here is not in piles, but spread out in even layers, apparently the result of water movement. In the lower-middle part of the cave deposit, the ash layer is thicker near the south wall. At its maximum, it is four metres deep. It was around the fringe of this ash layer that most of the human fossils and stone tools were unearthed. In November, 1936, the bottom part of the ash layer of this location yielded three complete human skulls. The ash layer at the lowest part of the deposit lies more than 30 metres below the top of the cave. The mandible of Peking Man found in 1959 was in the top of this layer, which had also yielded a maxilla (upper jaw) of Peking Man in 1937.

The term "ash" used here denotes substances in purple, red, yellow, white or black. Most of the black substance appears at the top or base of a layer, the ash deposit of other colours being sandwiched in between. These ashes are easily recognizable as they are brightly coloured, soft and wet, so much so, that if one squeezes a handful of them, water oozes out. When dry, they are very light.

Laboratory analysis reveals a large amount of carbon in the black substance, especially in the black ash from the bottom of the layer, where a piece of Chinese redbud wood charcoal was also found. All this strengthens the belief that the black substance is plant ash. Except for the difference in colours, the other substances seem to be

Evidence of Peking Man's use of fire: (1) Ash layers in the deposit in Peking Man's cave home.

(2) Charred bones.

(3) Burnt stone.

(4) Burnt earth containing plant ash.

materially the same as the black one. There is as yet no satisfactory explanation of the difference in colour between substances which are materially the same. Some hold that it may have been due to the different temperatures of different fires, and others believe it could be the result of different ways of burning.

Scorched stones and bones are numerous in the ash layers, especially in the black ones. Some of the scorched stones have changed colour while others are cracked or brittle. The burnt limestone has become lime. The scorched bones have turned black, blue, white, grey, green or dull brown. Many are cracked or twisted. Burnt hackberry seeds coloured black, blue and grey have also been found.

Did the Peking Man get the fire from nature, or did he make it himself? We deduce that he could preserve fire, but not make it. Naturally-occurring fire was not a practical source for him to rely on, yet fire was a powerful aid to his very survival without which he was in danger. So he knew he must preserve it, and he was very careful to do so.

Yet Peking Man was not the first human being to use fire, his ancestors had long before learned the technique of preserving fire, and handed it down from one generation to the next. This is proved by the presence of ashes and scorched bones at Locality 13 of Choukoutien, a cave home earlier than that of Peking Man. That is to say, man began to use fire at least half a million years ago.

It was no simple matter for primitive men to learn to preserve fire; the skill must have taken a long time to acquire. The first fire man had was no doubt from some natural occurrence, perhaps the burning of grass and trees by live lava from a volcanic eruption; a forest fire started by lightning; or the self-combustion of thick piles of dry grass or twigs.

When primitive men first saw a blazing fire with smoke rising in clouds and everything being burnt to ashes, they probably scurried for shelter in fright. Like other animals, many of them may have lost their lives in conflagrations. Being more developed than other animals, primitive men finally learnt from the better taste of roast meat that fire could be a force for good as well as for evil. Once they knew this, they learnt how to use fire for their own benefit and avoid its hazards. This was one of man's great discoveries, but it was not achieved in a short span of time, nor was it the feat of any single clever man. The long groping process may have lasted thousands of millennia.

The use of fire effected a tremendous change in man's life. Fire helped to assure his survival and to develop his rudimentary ability to control natural forces; it was a leap from quantitative to qualitative change.

Many animals, like primitive man, liked to live in caves, and man had to fight them for occupancy. With the help of fire, he won easily and thus ended his nomadic life. Now he had only to post one person, preferably at the cave entrance, to keep the fire burning and his home would be safe. While Peking Man inhabited Choukoutien, there must have been many hearths both inside and outside. Fires were damped down with moist twigs and earth, and could be revived again when they were needed.

Fire also provided light at night and heat in winter, thus man was partially freed from his dependence on sunlight and the fickle climate.

Man ate meat raw before he knew the use of fire, but afterwards he could roast the animals he caught which enabled him to accelerate his evolutionary process. This change in Peking Man's diet is proved by the presence of large quantities of charred animal bones in the ash layers of the cave deposit.

At present, the evidence of man's use of fire discovered at the cave home of Peking Man is the earliest and the clearest from any of the sites of human fossils which have been excavated. Once he had harnessed fire, man's development was greatly accelerated by the new material force which he controlled.

Peking Man's surroundings
and his life

The environs of Choukoutien

In the long period during which Peking Man made Choukoutien his home, it must have changed considerably in
its topography especially in the Pleistocene during which
there were several great glaciations. Changes of such
magnitude inevitably affected the fauna and flora.

Sporo-pollen analysis shows that only the basal gravel
layer at the bottom of the Peking Man's cave deposit was
formed under glacial conditions; all the layers which
yielded human fossils were formed under normal climatic
conditions similar to those of today. This proves beyond
doubt that it was during the interglacial ages that Peking
Man founded his colony here. However, sporo-pollen
analysis indicates that there were minor climatic changes.
It was colder when the lower layers were formed than
when the middle layers accumulated. Generally speaking,
judging from the characteristics of the flora, the climate
then must have been very similar to that of North China
today, a typical temperate one, with four distinctive sea-

Peking Man hunted and gathered fruit, herbs and tubers.

He made tools . . .

. . . and could preserve fire.

Reconstruction of a Chinese hyenas.

Reconstruction of a thick-jaw deer.

Reconstruction of a sabre-toothed tiger.

sons, thriving vegetation in summer, and leafless trees in winter.

Studies on the mammalian fossils bear this out. More fossils of cold temperate zone animals were found in the lower layers than those of warm temperate zone animals, indicating that the climate was colder during the formation of the lower layers. In the upper layers, (the 8th and 9th) there are as many fossils of cold temperate animals as lower down, but those of the warm temperate animals increase considerably, indicating that the climate was becoming warmer. This trend continues in the 7th and 6th layers until at last the amount of the fossils of cold temperate animals begin to decrease and the other species predominate. But the 5th layer shows a temporary reverse of the trend, as the fossils of cold temperate animals increase again, indicating a change to a colder climate. In the upper 4th layer (the one with the thickest ash deposit), a switch to a very warm climate is shown by the complete disappearance of fossils of the cold temperate animals and a further increase in those of the other species. We may infer that the 4th layer dates from the warmest period of the age in which the deposit formed. After that, a more moderate climate set in, for the top layers formed later in Peking Man's occupation of the cave once more contain the fossils of cold temperate animals, though they are outnumbered by the other species. This indicates that it was still warm, but cooler than at the time of the formation of the 4th layer.

These mammals as a whole belong to the species of the northern temperate zone, only very rarely do we see a species associated with tropical or polar climates. Climatic studies based on fossil remains have produced results essentially consistent with those obtained through sporo-pollen analysis.

With evidence from research on fossil remains and sporo-pollen analysis, we can build up quite a detailed picture of Choukoutien at the time of Peking Man, especially in the middle period of his presence in the area.

In the mountainous areas to the north and west of the present town of Choukoutien, mixed forests of pines, cedars, elms, hackberries, and Chinese redbuds were inhabited by such animals as big macacos, bisons, sabre-toothed tigers, tigers, leopards, brown bears, black bears, red dogs, raccoon dogs and wolves. The lush growth of goosefoot, lily, sagebrush and pyrola on the vast grassland to the southeast sheltered animals such as the cheetah, the horse, the woolly rhinoceros, the striped hyena, the glutton, the sika deer and the elephant. There was a big river to the east of Dragon Bone Hill, and probably a lake as well. In the shallow water grew pondweed, parrot feather and bullrushes, and along the river banks and lake shore, willows made shady spots where the buffalo liked to wallow. In late autumn, thick-jaw deer migrated here. Otters, beavers and giant beavers swam in the river.

How Peking Man hunted and gathered

The daily life of Peking Man should not be thought of as an easy one with frequent feasts of roast venison. Actually, primitive man would only exceptionally have succeeded in killing a big animal. The difficulties which confronted him are hard for us to conceive.

For all the nearly two million years of evolution since the first stone tools had been made by the earliest primitive man, Peking Man still retained many primitive characteristics. It would take many more years of labour and struggle for man to evolve into what he is today. Primitive as he was, his hunting gear consisting only of clubs and rocks supplemented sometimes by a torch when needed, it was quite impossible for Peking Man to hunt down big animals at will.

Among the mass of stone tools found at Choukoutien, none can be identified as a weapon for hunting. The big choppers would have been good only for cutting firewood or shaping hunting clubs, not as weapons. The big scrapers with concave edges were probably useful for scraping wooden clubs, but, of course, no trace of the clubs has survived.

Peking Man did no doubt hunt, as even his much earlier ancestors had done. He could have killed big prey by running it down and hitting it with rocks. But almost all animals that are not ferocious are swift. Judging by the fossil remains, the commonest big animals were the sika and the thick-jaw deer, whose sense organs are acute, and who are extremely wary. Sometimes they may also be aggressive, charging their foes with their antlers aimed at the abdomen. Wild pigs and bears, whose fossils occur in the cave in great numbers, are fierce creatures. The boar is especially daring, undaunted even when faced with a tiger, and when wounded, it becomes all the more violent. The brown bear is also strong and ferocious; it sometimes makes surprise attacks on man. All this shows how rare it must have been for Peking Man to hunt down a big beast. That he did once in a while succeed in doing so was not due to physical force; he used his wits too, otherwise, even an occasional success would have been impossible. Living alongside wild animals he would certainly have come to know their habits, and found ways of dealing with them. He had probably learnt to hunt in an intelligent way, taking advantage for example of natural features, such as cliffs, rock barriers, mires or narrow passes where his quarry could be hemmed in and forced to plunge to its death or be killed.

His daily fare no doubt consisted more often of small animals such as hedgehogs, frogs, rats, bats and hares. The ash layers abound in their fossils, especially those of hamsters, mice, black rats and harvest mice, which sometimes constitute a thin layer of their own.

As Engels said, **"Exclusively hunting tribes, such as figure in books, i.e., tribes subsisting** *solely* **by hunting, have never existed, for the fruits of the chase are much too precarious to make that possible."***

Peking Man must have found out how, what and where to gather plants for food. He gathered not only edible herbs, wild fruit and tubers, but also ostrich eggs. A lot of fragments of egg-shell have been found, many of them charred. Further evidence is to be seen in the pointed bone and antler tools which, as we have said, were probably used for grubbing up tubers.

Hackberry seeds are present in the deposit, many of them charred and in pieces. To date, these are the only remains of Peking Man's plant food. Hackberry fruit is

---

* *The Origin of the Family, Private Property and the State,* Eng. ed., FLPH, Moscow, 1948, p. 35.

round, has a reddish-yellow flesh and tastes sweet. The white meat inside its seed is rich in starch and also edible. In any case, the Peking Man ate any edibles that he could lay his hands on; escape from hunger was his main preoccupation.

His power to resist the menace of natural forces was limited, as can be seen from his crude tools. His life was harsh and its span was short.

Studies based on fossil remains reveal the following statistics:

Approximate age at death	Per cent of fossils found to date
Under 14	39.5
15-30	7.0
40-50	7.9
50-60	2.6
Not clear	43.0

Obviously in Peking Man's time, no idler could have been tolerated. To feed the population alone required that each able-bodied person, regardless of age or sex, work hard from morning to night; even children had to help as much as they could by gathering firewood or stone materials for tool-making.

A head count of the colony at Choukoutien would be impossible, though a few score at any given time may be a reasonable guess. A larger colony would have been hard to feed, and a smaller one would have been too weak to fight natural disasters.

It was indeed a harsh existence, gathering and hunting all day long just to subsist. Countless lives must have been lost in struggles against wild animals and natural forces. Yet, with industry and intelligence, the human species represented by Peking Man defied all difficulties, survived the rigour of untamed nature and nurtured its young from generation to generation. Precisely because of his labour and his undaunted spirit in struggling against natural forces, man and his society were able to develop continuously over the long ages. Taking the evolutionary course as a whole, man seems to have remained unchanged in the early period for stretches of time as long as 100,000 or 200,000 years. Such in fact was not the case, for more profound analysis has proved that there were some changes between the earlier and later men in that period. This shows that the wheel of history turns inexorably on, and nothing can stop its forward movement.

Human palaeontology and archaeology in China

The disciplines of human palaeontology and archaeology gained academic recognition rather late in China, only about 50 years ago. Before liberation, these two fields, like other sciences, were heavily influenced by the semi-colonial and semi-feudal nature of society. In those days, the fossils of Peking Man, and even the right to research on them belonged to aliens, who thus controlled the direction that research took. Chinese scientists were barred from doing research on the human fossils they found.

During the War of Resistance Against Japan and the War of Liberation, when under reactionary regimes times were so hard that even survival became a problem for the ordinary working people, it was of course quite impossible to carry out scientific research. Until liberation in 1949, research on Peking Man was completely suspended.

Progress in archaeology and palaeontology gained great impetus from the new turn of events, for as new construction projects started up all over the country, valuable and important relics kept coming to light, inspiring further research on a much larger scale. In view of the new situation, all stages of the work, from survey and excavation to research, instead of being in the charge of specialized institutes of the Chinese Academy of Sciences alone, were delegated to provincial museums, college departments and geological agencies. Thanks to closely coordinated efforts, this has resulted in a long run of new successes.

It should be emphasized that the rapid progress in this field in China cannot be disassociated from the correct leadership of the Chinese Communist Party and the ardent support of the masses. The Chinese Academy of Sciences and its institutes have had a stream of mail from every part of China written by people from all walks of life reporting new discoveries. Indeed, many sites which proved to be of great importance were found with this sort of help from ordinary people.

The general picture is quite different from before liberation. Ever since the people took over the reins of these scientific activities, there has not only been a complete change of outlook, the work as a whole has advanced much faster. More people are involved, facilities have greatly increased, and far more sites are under exploration. Whereas in the past, only Choukoutien and a few other sites were being worked on, with enthusiastic support of the agencies concerned and of the masses, the work has now been extended to sites all over the country.

List of sites and finds

1957, Hsiaolungtan,[1] *Kaiyuan County,*[2] *Yunnan Province.* Five fossil teeth of the *Ramapithecus* of the early Pliocene, roughly ten million years old, were found in a coal deposit. Scientists believe this genus of prehominid is the direct ancestor of a primitive man who had not known how to make tools.

1965, Yuanmou County, Yunnan Province. Two fossil incisors of Yuanmou Man[3] of the early Pleistocene about a million years old were unearthed. These finds, in addition to those already discussed, provide clear evidence that China was one of the areas where the human species originated.

1961-62, Hsihoutu Village, Juicheng County, Shansi Province. This site has yielded artifacts dating back more than a million years (Villafranchian). No human fossil has been found. The few score of stone implements found include cores, flakes, scrapers and choppers, crudely fashioned upon pebbles or boulders. Large number of fossil vertebrates were found along with these stone tools. A stone tool corresponding in time to the artifacts at this site has come to light at a site in the Nihowan bed, Yangyuan County, Hopei Province. The owner has not yet been identified, as no human fossil has been found. Nevertheless, this evidence proves that at least a million years ago, the ancestors of man had spread along the periphery of latitute 40°15′ north, longitude 114°21′ east — the farthest northeastern region in China in which relics of primeval culture have ever been found.

1960, Keho Village,[4] Juicheng County, Shansi Province. This site has yielded artifacts comparable in age with the finds at Locality 13 of Choukoutien, predating Peking Man. The stone tools were contained in the gravel layer beneath reddish earth. They include choppers, scrapers, points and big prismatic points, which are generally rougher and bigger than similar tools of Peking Man.

1963-65, Chenchiawo[5] and Kungwangling[6] villages of Lantien County, Shensi Province. These sites have at different times yielded a mandible, a skull-cap and artifacts of Lantien Man,[7] along with fossil vertebrates. Analysis of the deposit, and the characteristics of the human fossils have led scientists to believe that these predate Peking Man.

In recent years a few sites in north and south China have yielded stone tools roughly contemporary to or a little later than those of Peking Man. Early Palaeolithic artifacts and fossil vertebrates abound in the Kuanyin Cave,[8] Shawo Village,[9] Chienhsi County,[10] Kweichow Province. Excavations were carried out at this site in 1964, 1965 and 1972. Another cave site at Shihlungtou,[11] Tayeh County,[12] Hupeh Province, yielded in 1972 stone tools possibly of the same period.

Human fossils and cultural finds of the Middle Palaeolithic Period unearthed from the early Late Pleistocene deposits (100,000-40,000 years old) have been much richer in quantity. They include a skull-cap of "Mapa Man," unearthed in 1959 at a site in Shaokuan, Kwangtung Province, and a maxilla of "Changyang Man," dug up in Changyang County, Hupeh Province, in 1957. Most significant of all was the discovery of "Tingtsun Man" in 1954, at Tingtsun Village, Hsiangfen County, Shansi Province. The site yielded three juvenile teeth along with great numbers of stone tools and fossil vertebrates. The finds represent an important link in the continuity of primeval culture in China. More surveys and excavations in a wider

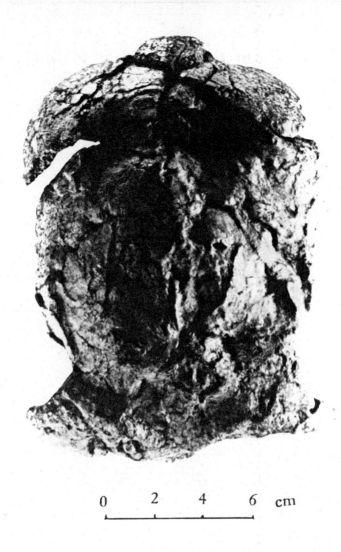

0 2 4 6 cm

Cranium of Lantien Man.

Lantien, Shensi Province, where Lantien Man was discovered in 1963-64. Lower right are his reconstructed cranium and mandible.

Early Pleistocene site at Hsihoutu Village, Juicheng County, Shansi Province, and some stone tools found there. (1 & 2) Quartzite cores. (3) Quartzite choppers. (4) Concave-edged flint scraper.

Early Pleistocene site at Nihowan, Yangyuan County, Hopei Province, and a shaped stone found there.

0   1   2   3cm

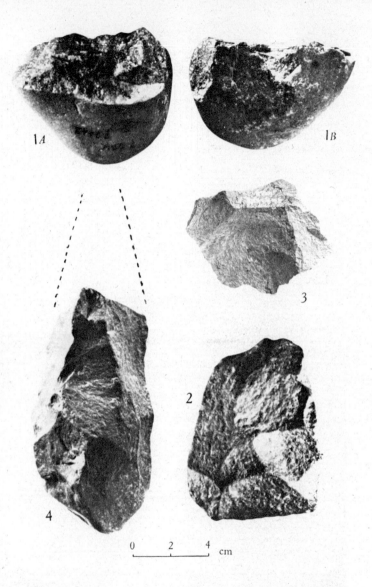

Stone tools from an early Middle Pleistocene site at Keho Village, Juicheng County, Shansi Province. (1 & 2) Quartzite choppers chipped on both sides. (3) Quartzite core. (4) Heavy point made of a triangular flake.

area have proved that the Tingtsun culture extended along the whole valley of the Fenho River, indicating that some 100,000 years ago, the region played host to a thriving human community.

Finds from the Late Palaeolithic deposits (dating back 40,000-10,000 years) have come to light in still greater numbers. An important one was "Liuchiang Man,"[13] unearthed in 1959, in Liuchiang County, Kwangsi Chuang Autonomous Region. A list of other finds follows:

Human occipital, artifacts and fossil vertebrates, unearthed in 1963, at Chihyu Village,[14] Shuohsien County,[15] Shansi Province. The artifacts include bone and stone implements and perforated graphite ornaments. The fossil vertebrates like those found along the Sjara-osso-gol River[16] in Inner Mongolia, date from the early Late Palaeolithic. A radiocarbon test indicates a date of around 28,135 years B.P. The stone tools include choppers, small points and scrapers, planing tools, round scrapers, arrowheads and engraving-tools (or burins) in various shapes. Uniformly small in size, they resemble the microliths of the Mesolithic and Neolithic often seen in northern China.

Some scientists used to hold that this microlith culture originated in Siberia and spread southwards to the Great Wall area. The finds unearthed at the Chihyu site have proved the contrary — the culture radiated out from northern China, to areas far beyond the Great Wall belt. The evidence so far available attests that the culture extended as far as latitude 34°1' to the north near Hsuchang,[17] Honan Province, on the North China Plain; and to the southwest as far as the foot of the Himalayas, for there are sites in Nyanang County,[18] Tibet, 4,300 metres above sea level.

Judging from the materials available to us at present, no other culture in the world can rival that of the Chihyu microliths in antiquity. Stone arrowheads of the Late Palaeolithic Era have been found in western Europe and North Africa, but they do not seem to predate those at Chihyu.

Small stone tools, of the Late Palaeolithic, unearthed at the town of Fulin,[19] Hanyuan County,[20] Szechuan Province. First discovered in the early 1960s, the site was again surveyed and excavated in 1972, and more materials were obtained, which confirm the previous dating.

Stone tools and fossil vertebrates, unearthed from a cave deposit at Hsiaonanhai,[21] Anyang County,[22] Honan Province, in 1960. The tools are generally small in size, similar to microliths. After a comprehensive study, a date of the later Late Palaeolithic was assigned to them, which is contemporary to or a little later than the Sjara-osso-gol River finds and earlier than the Upper Cave Man culture of Choukoutien.

Stone tools, unearthed from the sandy yellow earth at Pachienfang,[23] Lingyuan County,[24] Liaoning Province, in 1972. The date is probably the end of the Late Palaeolithic. They are made of flint, rock crystal and agate, and resemble microliths.

Some revised findings

The new evidence obtained through re-excavation or further research on old sites has resulted in the revision of some theories. A brief summary follows:

Lineage of the Upper Cave Man. In 1961, an inten-
sive study of the models of the Upper Cave Man led scientists to conclude that the Upper Cave Man was a primitive
Mongoloid type, akin to the Chinese, Eskimo and American
Indian. The Upper Cave Man's fossils date from a time
when the Mongoloid race had almost taken form, with
only a few minor characteristics as yet undeveloped. This
negates the earlier theory that the Upper Cave Man and
his family were members of a tribe who came to Choukoutien and were subsequently extinguished in attacks
upon them by the native Chinese.

Evolution of Peking Man. A study has recently been
made by young Chinese scientists on various Peking Man
skull-caps. They compared several from the lower layers
of the cave deposit with one of a later period unearthed
in 1966. They were able to show that there *are* differences
between the early and later Peking Man which indicate
progress, though they are of the same species. The old
belief that despite the lapse of tremendously long period,
no salient change took place in the cranium of Peking
Man during the whole course of his existence has thus
been challenged.

Dating of the Shuitungkou[25] site. The Shuitungkou site
in the Ningsia Hui Autonomous Region was identified as
belonging to the end of the Middle and beginning of
the Late Palaeolithic in the early 1920s. More surveys and
excavations in the early 1960s yielded a number of stone
tools and one perforated ornament made of ostrich egg
shell, which has pushed forward the dating of the site to
the later period of Late Palaeolithic.

Dating of the Sjara-osso-gol site. This Inner Mongolian
site was dated before liberation. New evidence obtained

through more surveys, better information on geological conditions of the area, and, most important of all, comparison with the finds from the Chihyu site in Shansi Province, have led to a reconsideration of the dating. Now both sites are believed to date from the beginning of the Late Palaeolithic.

Under the guidance of Chairman Mao's revolutionary line, Chinese archaeologists and palaeoanthropologists are now working assiduously to understand and transform nature, and to comprehend how man has come to be what he is today. Under the leadership of the Chinese Communist Party and with the support of the masses, they are doing field surveys and excavation and laboratory research, striving to scale the heights of science and so fulfil the hopes of Chairman Mao who has said: **"China . . . ought to have made a greater contribution to humanity."**

---

[1]小龙潭.   [2]开远县.   [3]"元谋人".   [4]匼河村.   [5]陈家窝村.   [6]公王岭村.
[7]"蓝田人".   [8]观音洞.   [9]沙窝.   [10]黔西县.   [11]石龙头.   [12]大冶.
[13]"柳江人".   [14]峙峪.   [15]朔县.   [16]萨拉乌苏河.   [17]许昌.   [18]聂拉木县.
[19]富林镇.   [20]汉源县.   [21]小南海.   [22]安阳县.   [23]八间房.   [24]凌源县.
[25]水洞沟.

"北 京 人" 之 家

贾兰坡 编写

＊

外文出版社出版（北京）

1975年（32开）第一版

编号：（英）7050—38

00070

7—E—1358p